What you need to know about the National Tests

KEY STAGE 2 NATIONAL TESTS: HOW THEY WORK

Pupils between the ages of 7 and 11 (Years 3–6) cover Key Stage 2 of the National Curriculum. In May of their final year of Key Stage 2 (Year 6), all pupils take written National Tests (commonly known as SATs) in the three most important subjects: English, Mathematics and Science. The tests are carried out in school, under the supervision of teachers, but are marked by examiners outside the school.

The tests help to find out what children have learned in the key subjects. They will also help parents and teachers to know whether children are reaching the national standards set out in the National Curriculum.

Each child will probably spend in total around $4\frac{1}{2}$ hours during one week in May sitting the tests. In Mathematics and Science most children will do two papers, and three in English.

The school sends the papers away to external examiners for marking. After being marked, the papers are returned to the school and results reported to parents by the end of July. With the results of the tests, you will also receive the results of assessments made by teachers in the classroom, based on the work your child has done during the school year. You will also receive a summary of the results for all pupils at the school, and for pupils nationally. This will help you to know how your child is doing compared with other children of the same age.

The report from your child's school will explain to you what the results show about your child's progress, strengths, particular achievements and targets for development. It will also explain how to follow up the results with your child's teachers and why the test results may be different from the teacher's assessment.

WHY THE KEY STAGE 2 NATIONAL TESTS ARE IMPORTANT

It is very important that children do as well as they can in their National Tests. Although the results should not be used by secondary schools to determine which children to give places to, they may be used in other ways. For example, the results could be used to determine which subject teaching group your child will be placed in. Good test results, together with a positive report from the primary school, will ensure your child is placed in a higher group. In turn, this means your child will study the higher levels of the Key Stage 3 curriculum.

LEVELS OF ACHIEVEMENT: KNOWING HOW WELL YOUR CHILD IS DOING

The National Curriculum divides each subject into a number of levels, from one to eight. On average, children are expected to advance one level for every two years they are at school. So, looking at the table overleaf, you will see that by Year 6 (the end of Key Stage 2), your child should be at Level 4. The table includes the levels for 7-, 11- and 14-year-olds (for the end of Key Stages 1, 2 and 3) to give you an overall picture of how your child should progress.

	Above Level 8	7 years	11 years	14 years

☐ Exceptional performance

■ Exceeded targets for age group

☐ Achieved targets for age group

■ Working towards targets for age group

	7 years	11 years	14 years
Above Level 8			☐
Level 8			■
Level 7			■
Level 6		☐	☐
Level 5		■	☐
Level 4	☐	☐	■
Level 3	■	■	■
Level 2	☐	■	■
Level 1	■	■	■

Your child compared with his or her age group

There are different National Tests papers for different ability levels. This is to ensure that pupils can take a test paper where they can show positive achievement, and not be discouraged by trying to answer questions which are too easy or too difficult. Most children will take the two papers for Levels 3–5 in Science. Each paper will be 35 minutes long. Extension papers with high level questions are also available for exceptionally bright pupils.

This book concentrates on Levels 3–5, giving plenty of practice to help your child achieve the best level possible. There are also some higher level questions for very able pupils. Do not worry if your child cannot do these questions. If he or she can reach Level 5 having done the main questions, then your child will already be above the average for his or her age. The table below shows you what percentage of pupils nationally reached each of the levels in the 1994 tests for Science.

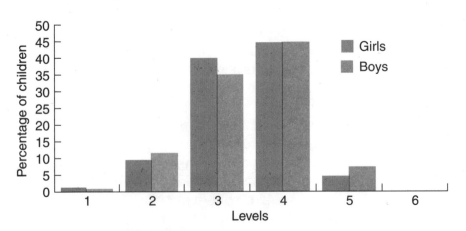

Levels achieved in Science, 1994

SCIENCE AT KEY STAGE 2

The questions in this book will help you prepare your child by testing him or her on the Key Stage 2 curriculum for Science. For assessment purposes, the National Curriculum divides Science into four sections, called Attainment Targets (ATs). The first AT, Scientific Investigation, is assessed only by the teacher in the classroom, not in the written tests. The other three ATs are:

AT2: Life Processes and Living Things (which is largely Biology)
AT3: Materials and their Properties (which is largely Chemistry)
AT4: Physical Processes (which is largely Physics)

The Science National Curriculum defines level descriptions for each of the four ATs. These are taken together to give an overall level for Science. The test papers have questions covering ATs 2–4. National Test questions are designed to assess your child's ability in four areas:

Knowledge and understanding
Handling information
Interpretation and evaluation
Problem solving

The questions in this book cover these skills.

USING THIS BOOK TO HELP YOUR CHILD PREPARE FOR THE NATIONAL TEST IN SCIENCE

This book contains four basic features:

Questions:	two test papers for Levels 3–5, and one extension paper for Level 6
Answers:	showing acceptable responses and marks
Note to Parent:	giving advice to help improve your child's score and ensure that common mistakes are not made
Level chart:	showing you how to interpret your child's marks to arrive at a level.

Details of how to run the tests at home are given below. Information about how to mark the tests and assess your child can be found on page 49. Try setting Test A, mark the test and see how your child does, and work through the advice together. Then, a little later, try Test B and see whether your child has improved. Do not set your child Test C unless he or she has done very well in Tests A and B.

In the margin of each question page, there are small boxes. These are divided in half, with the marks available for that question at the bottom, and a blank at the top for you to fill in your child's score.

SIMULATING TEST CONDITIONS

Each test should take about 35–40 minutes. Let your child carry out the test in a place where he or she is comfortable. Your child will need a pencil and a ruler. Answers should be written in the spaces in this book. Tell your child to show as much reasoning with the answers as possible. The number of lines, or the space left, is an indication of the length of answer required. If your child has not finished after 40 minutes allow extra time until he or she finishes.

If your child cannot read a word you may read it out to him or her. If he or she does not understand a word you can explain what it means, providing it is not a scientific word. For example, you can explain what is meant by the word 'label' but not 'force' or 'evaporate'.

An alternative strategy you could employ is to work through Test A with your child after you have spent some time reading the answers and advice. You can then show your child what has to be done. Then, hopefully, he or she can carry on with Test B with confidence about what is required.

MARKING THE QUESTIONS
Guidance on how to mark your child's answers to the questions is given on page 49.

FINALLY, AS THE TESTS DRAW NEAR
In the days before the tests, make sure your child is as relaxed and confident as possible. You can help by:

- ensuring your child knows what test papers he or she will be doing and how to answer them.

- working through practice questions, and discussing which answers are right and why.

- checking that your child has all the relevant equipment, such as a pencil and a ruler

Look out for signs of anxiety, such as changes in eating or sleeping habits. Although many children look forward to tests, it is only natural that some may be nervous. Reassure your child that, though very important, the tests are not the only means by which he or she will be assessed.

Instructions

Read all the words carefully. Look at any diagrams or pictures which should help you.

The questions for you to answer are in orange boxes.

For example:

Give the names of the pieces of apparatus shown in the picture.

Look for the ▭⇒ to show you where to write your answer.

Remember to explain your answers if you are asked to do so.

GOOD LUCK!

Name ....

Start		Finish	

1   Ali went to visit a nearby pond in a farmer's field.

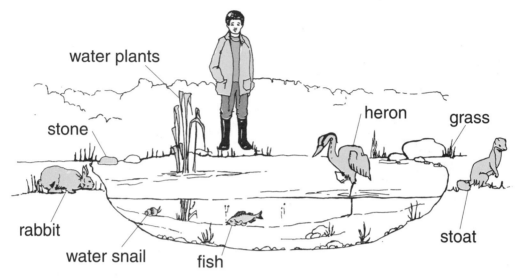

Ali, the birds and fish are all living things.

a   One food chain shown in the picture is:

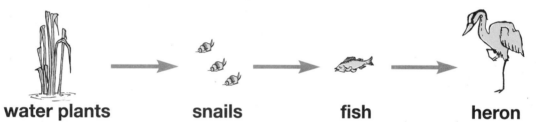

water plants	**snails**	**fish**	**heron**

(i)   **Write down the name of the producer in this food chain.**

....

(ii)   Pollution of the pond kills all of the fish.

What might happen to the heron?

....

b   Look back at the picture of the pond again.

Complete another food chain

.... ➡ .... ➡ ....

1
Q1a(i)

1
Q1a(ii)

3
Q1b

Visit to
the pond

3

Q1c

c   **Tick THREE boxes to show THREE things Ali, the birds and fish must do to stay alive.**

 eat food   ☐

lay eggs   ☐

swim   ☐

breathe   ☐

fly   ☐

lose waste materials   ☐

d   Ali turned over a large stone. Underneath the stone he found a number of woodlice.

Write down THREE reasons why woodlice would prefer to live under the stone rather than on the surface of the earth.

3

Q1d

 (i) ....

(ii) ....

(iii) ....

2   The picture shows plants growing around an oak tree in springtime.

a   **Why are there few plants growing in the shaded ground under the tree? Write down TWO reasons.**

 (i) ....

(ii) ....

Bluebells are woodland plants that grow in spring. They produce blue or white flowers.

b   **Write down ONE way in which the bluebell is suited to its environment.**

....

The bird in the drawing is a woodpecker. Woodpeckers eat insects.

c   **Write down ONE way in which the woodpecker is suited to its environment.**

 ....

d   The leaf litter in the wood is home to many animals and micro-organisms.

What important job do the micro-organisms in the leaf litter do?

....

2
Q2a

1
Q2b

1
Q2c

1
Q2d

3

The body

3 The drawing shows some organs in the body.

The organs are:

| brain | heart | kidney | lung | stomach |

B ....

C ....

D ....

A ....

E ....

5
Q3a

a | Add labels to the organs labelled A, B, C, D and E on the diagram. |

b | Each of the body organs has a job to do. In the table write the **LETTER** of the correct organ next to its job in the table. |

5
Q3b

Job	Organ
pumps the blood round the body	
digests food	
filters the blood	
exchanges gases	
controls the body's actions	

4 The graph shows how the height of a girl changes from the age of five to eighteen years old.

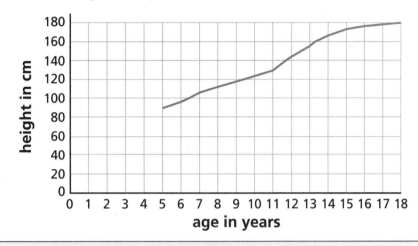

a How tall was the girl when she was eight years old?

Q4a
1

b How much did she grow between her fifth and eleventh birthdays?

Q4b
1

c How old was she when she started to grow faster?

Q4c
1

d When she was born the girl was 50 cm tall. Put an X on the graph to show this.

Q4d
1

e On her third birthday the girl was 80 cm tall. Put an X on the graph to show this.

Q4e
1

f Draw a line through the crosses and join it to the line on the graph. Did she grow faster between birth and three years old or between three and five years old?

Q4f
1

Letts

A new life

5   Sunil's mother tells him that she is pregnant, and he will be having a new brother or sister.

The words in the list describe the stages that the new baby will go through in its life.

**adolescence   childhood   infancy   middle age
retirement   young adulthood**

a   Arrange the list in the correct order, starting when the baby is born.

....

....

b   At which stage in the list is Sunil's new brother or sister most likely to have a child of his or her own?

....

c   During which stages will Sunil's new brother or sister be growing?

....

....

Making pure water

6 In an African village some people were trying to make some drinking water from very muddy water from a small stream.

a They first poured some of the muddy water through a clean cloth into a clean metal can.

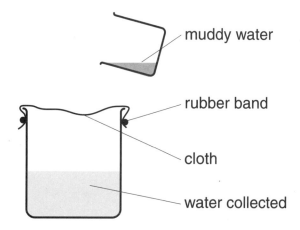

muddy water

rubber band

cloth

water collected

(i) | **What sort of cloth should they use?**

....

1

Q6a(i)

(ii) | **What will happen to the mud as the water goes through the cloth?**

....

....

1

Q6a(ii)

(iii) | **What impurities will remain in the water after passing through the cloth?**

....

1

Q6a(iii)

(iv) | **What do we call this way of separation?**

....

1

Q6a(iv)

7

Making pure water

b They then heated the water using the apparatus shown.

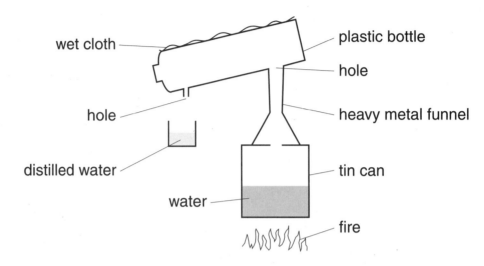

wet cloth — plastic bottle — hole — heavy metal funnel — hole — distilled water — water — tin can — fire

1
Q6b(i)

(i) What happens to the water in the tin can when it is heated?

....

1
Q6b(ii)

(ii) What happens in the plastic bottle?

....

1
Q6b(iii)

(iii) Why is the wet cloth put on the outside of the plastic bottle?

....

1
Q6b(iv)

(iv) Underline the word which best describes what is happening in the diagram.

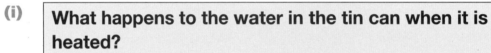 condensation   chromotography   distillation   evaporation

1
Q6b(v)

(v) Where are the impurities which were dissolved in the water?

....

8

Making a car

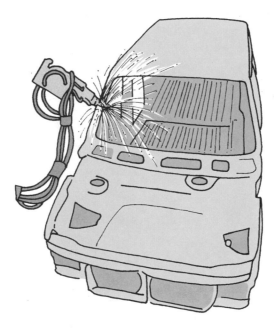

7   Copper, paint, plastic, rubber and steel are used when cars are made.

Tick the box which shows why car makers use materials.

a   Electric wiring in the car is made from **copper** because copper

☐   ... is shiny.
☐   ... is not magnetic.
☐   ... is a conductor of electricity.

1
Q7a

b   Car tyres are made of **rubber** because rubber

☐   ... is black.
☐   ... is squashy.
☐   ... is made from the sap of the rubber tree.

1
Q7b

c   Car steering wheels can be made of **plastic** because plastic

☐   ... is easily shaped.
☐   ... is heavy.
☐   ... does not conduct.

1
Q7c

8   Here are some materials which may be used in making a car. Some of these materials are **natural** and some have been **made**.

> Tick **ONE** box for each material to show if it is **made** or **natural**.

	Natural	Made
(i) glass	☐	☐
(ii) steel	☐	☐
(iii) water	☐	☐
(iv) plastic	☐	☐
(v) wood	☐	☐

9   The table shows some properties of solids, liquids and gases.

Property	Solid	Liquid	Gas
hard	yes	no	no
can flow easily	no	yes	yes
can be squashed easily	no	no	yes

> Use the table to finish these sentences. One has been done for you.

a   The door handle of a car is made of a .... *solid*

because ... *the handle is hard and cannot be squashed.*

b   The oil in the car engine is a ....

because ....

c   The car tyre is filled with ....

because ....

Containers

10 The picture shows five liquids in their containers.

a Write down **THREE** materials used to make these containers.

....

b Some of the **liquids** are see-through and others are not see-through.

Finish the table. One has been done for you.

See-through	Not see-through
bleach	

11

Letts

Dissolving

11 A spoonful of blue copper sulphate crystals is added to 100 cm³ of cold water.

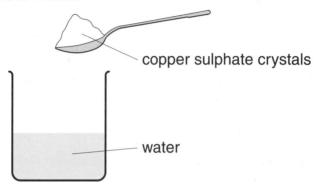

copper sulphate crystals

water

The crystals dissolve and form a copper sulphate solution.

a **Write down TWO ways of dissolving the copper sulphate crystals more quickly.**

(i) ....

(ii) ....

b **How does copper sulphate solution look different from water?**

....

A hot saturated solution of copper sulphate dissolved in water was allowed to cool.

c **What would be formed?**

....

d **How would the result be different if the solution had been cooled quickly?**

....

Letts

The table contains information about copper sulphate and copper oxide.

Substance	Solubility in cold water
copper sulphate	soluble
copper oxide	insoluble

e **Describe how copper sulphate could be produced from a mixture of copper sulphate and copper oxide solids.**
Write your answer or draw labelled diagrams.

....

....

....

....

....

or

4

Q11e

13

MARKS

12 Some children record the position of the Sun from their classroom window. They do this by looking at the Sun through some dark glass.

The drawing shows the position of the Sun in the morning and afternoon of a day in winter.

morning   afternoon

1
Q12a

a **Draw a circle to show where they would see the Sun at midday.**

b The children track the Sun by marking the shadow of a pole in the playground. The drawing shows the shadow they saw in the morning.

Draw and label the shadows they would see at midday and in the afternoon.

2
Q12b

13 There was a full Moon on 25 May.

> **Underline the possible date of the next full Moon after this.**

 1 June　　　　**9 June**　　　　**16 June**　　　　**23 June**

 1
Q13

14 The drawing shows the Earth, the Sun and the Moon.

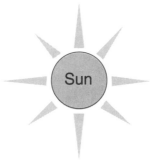

Sun

Moon
Earth

Not to scale

 1
Q14a

a **Shade in the part of the Earth where it is night.**

b During the next twenty-four hours the night changes to day and back to night.

> **Explain what causes this.**

 2
Q14b

....

....

15 Sandy is making a model to show how the Sun, Earth and Moon are arranged.

> **Choose the things she should use by placing a tick next to one thing in each column in the table.**

Sun	Earth	Moon
cushion	tennis ball	apple
cardboard box	bag of sugar	sugar cube
football	sugar cube	football
apple	grape	table-tennis ball

 3
Q15

In the park

16 In autumn, leaves fall from the trees.

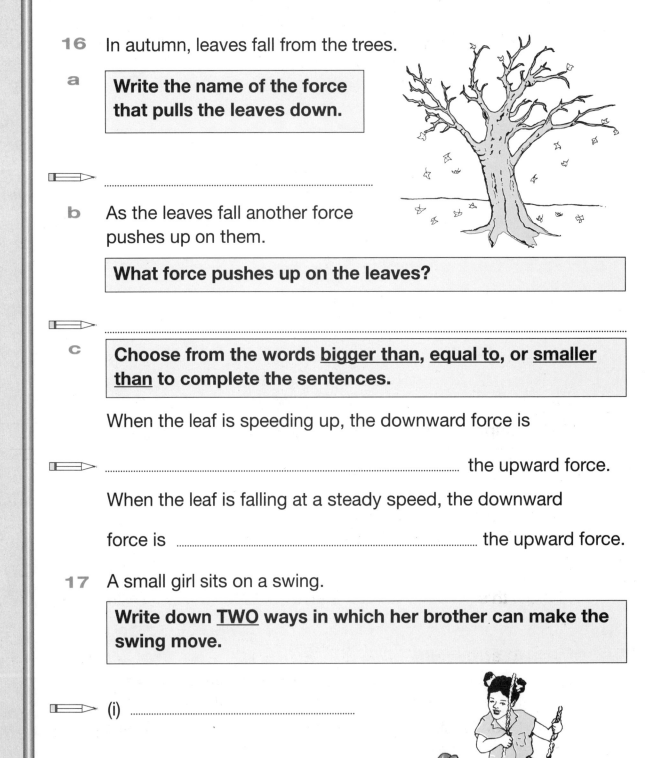

a | **Write the name of the force that pulls the leaves down.**

....

b As the leaves fall another force pushes up on them.

What force pushes up on the leaves?

....

c | **Choose from the words <u>bigger than</u>, <u>equal to</u>, or <u>smaller than</u> to complete the sentences.**

When the leaf is speeding up, the downward force is

.... the upward force.

When the leaf is falling at a steady speed, the downward

force is .... the upward force.

17 A small girl sits on a swing.

Write down <u>TWO</u> ways in which her brother can make the swing move.

(i) ....

....

(ii) ....

....

18 Gemma throws her ball straight up into the air.

a | **What happens to the speed of the ball as it goes up?**

....

1
Q18a

b | **Why does the ball fall down again?**

....

1
Q18b

c The **Earth's pull** and **air resistance** act on the ball as it falls down.

| **Use an arrow labelled E and an arrow labelled A to mark these forces on the drawing of the ball falling down.**

2
Q18c

d | **Which force is bigger, the Earth's pull or air resistance?**

....

1
Q18d

e | **How could you tell that this force is bigger?**

....

1
Q18e

Letts

In the park

19 Robert is walking in the park holding a balloon. The balloon is filled with helium.
Helium is a gas which is lighter than air.
One force on the balloon has been marked on the drawing.

Upward push from the air

a | **What will happen to the balloon if Robert lets go of it?**

1
Q19a

....

....

b | **Explain why this will happen.**

3
Q19b

....

....

20 Some children are playing on some bouncy toys in the park.

a | **What happens to the spring when a child sits on it?**

1
Q20a

....

b | **Why does this happen?**

1
Q20b

....

....

21 Sam builds a toy car and puts a magnet on it.

He finds that he can **push** the car along by holding another magnet near to it.

a **Draw an arrow on the car to show which way it moves when it is *pushed* by the magnet.**

Q21a

b **Shade the right-hand magnet to show how Sam must hold it so that it *pushes* the car.**

Q21b

c Sam uses a magnet to pick up a paper clip.
The arrow on the drawing shows the force that is pulling the paper clip down.

Q21c

Draw an arrow to show the other force on the paper clip.

Sam places two magnets on a table with a paper clip between them.

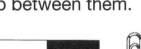 

2
Q21d

d **Draw arrows on the paper clip to show the pulls from the magnets.**

e **Which way does the paper clip move?**

1
Q21e

f Where should Sam put the paper clip so that it does not move? Draw it on the picture.

Q21f

Test B
Keys

Start		Finish	

1 Ian found three small animals and used a key to find out what they were.

Here is the key.

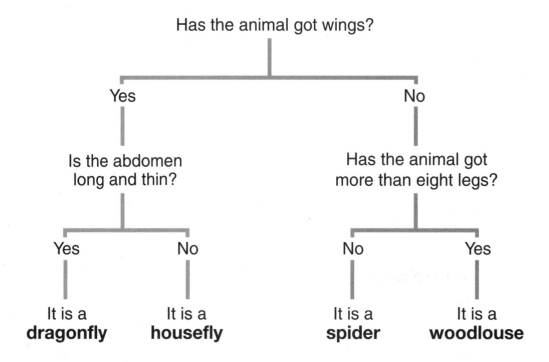

Has the animal got wings?

Yes → Is the abdomen long and thin?
 Yes → It is a **dragonfly**
 No → It is a **housefly**

No → Has the animal got more than eight legs?
 No → It is a **spider**
 Yes → It is a **woodlouse**

Write the names of the three small animals Ian found underneath the pictures.

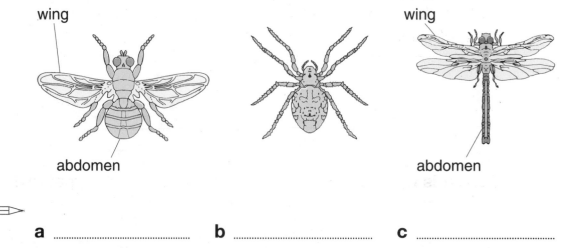

a .... b .... c ....

1 Q1a

1 Q1b

1 Q1c

20

Growing plants

2   The diagram shows a bean plant.

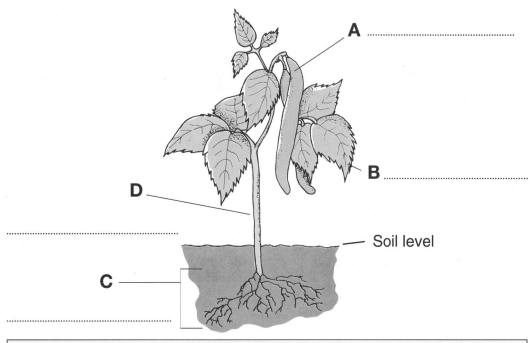

A ....

B ....

D

....

Soil level

C

....

a   **Add labels to the diagram above, using words from the list below.**

4

Q2a

flower   fruit   leaf   root   seed   stem

b   **Write down the letter A, B, C or D which gives the part of the plant which has seeds inside.**

1

Q2b

....

c   **Write down the letter A, B, C or D which shows the part of the plant which takes in water.**

1

Q2c

....

Information in the seeds is passed on to the next generation of plants.

d   **What is it in the seed which passes on the information?**

1

Q2d

....

21

Growing plants

3 The diagram shows some of the important parts of a flower.

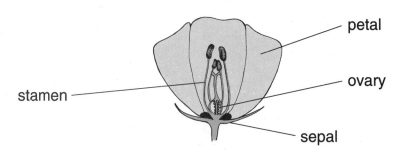

petal

ovary

stamen

sepal

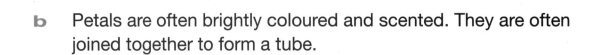

a | **Which is the male part of the flower?**

 ....

b Petals are often brightly coloured and scented. They are often joined together to form a tube.

(i) | **What is the job of the petals?**

....

(ii) | **Why do the petals do the job well?**

....

....

Feeding

4 The drawing shows some of the teeth in your mouth.

incisor — canine

molar

a Write down the job of each type of tooth.

(i) incisor ....

(ii) canine ....

(iii) molar ....

1 Q4a(i)

1 Q4a(ii)

1 Q4a(iii)

b Which type of tooth has sharp edges?

....

The picture shows a mouth.

Plaque on teeth is a mixture of food, microbes and acids.

plaque

1 Q4b

c Why is it important to remove plaque from teeth?

....

1 Q4c

d How can plaque be removed from teeth?

....

1 Q4d

e When are the best times of day to remove plaque from teeth?

....

1 Q4e

5 The drawing shows Shamira, a ten-year-old girl who lives in Africa. She is not ill but she is not as healthy as most ten-year-old girls who live in Britain.

Write down **THREE** reasons which could explain why Shamina is not very healthy.

(i) ....

(ii) ....

(iii) ....

1 Q5(i)

1 Q5(ii)

1 Q5(iii)

23

Blood round your body

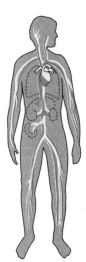

6 The drawing shows an organ system.

a Which organ system is shown in the drawing?

b Label the heart with a letter H.

c What important job does the heart do?

d Explain why this job is important.

e Blood travels to the leg muscles in an **artery** and returns to the heart in a **vein**.

Describe **TWO** differences between the blood in the artery and the blood in the vein.

7 As part of a science experiment, Jemma is fitted with a device that measures her pulse rate throughout the day. The chart shows her pulse rate at playtime.

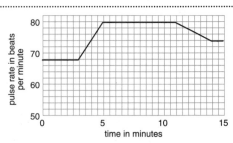

a At the beginning of playtime, Jemma sat down to have a drink and an apple.

How long did Jemma spend sitting down?

b After having her drink, Jemma played football with her friends.

How can you tell when Jemma started to play football?

Eleven minutes into playtime, Jemma's pulse rate started to go down.

c | **Suggest why this happened.**

1
Q7c

....

d | **What was Jemma's pulse rate at the end of playtime?**

1
Q7d

....

8   The service station sells different fuels.

a | **Complete the sentences by filling in words from the following list.**

| **burns** | **carbon dioxide** | **combustion** | **energy** |
| **evaporation** | **melts** | **oxygen** | **waste gases** |

5
Q8a

A fuel is a material which .... to release

.... and produce ....

When a fuel burns it uses up ....

from the air.

Another word for burning is ....

b | **Write down the name of a solid fuel, a liquid fuel and a gas fuel sold at the service station.**

Solid fuel ....

2
Q8b

Liquid fuel ....

Gas fuel ....

The service station

c   Here are two lists. The first is a list of raw materials and the second is a list of products made from them. All of the products are seen in the service station.

Draw a line to join each of the materials to the products made from it. One has been done for you.

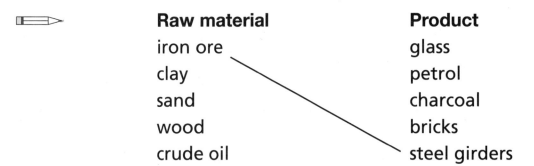

Raw material	Product
iron ore	glass
clay	petrol
sand	charcoal
wood	bricks
crude oil	steel girders

4

Q8c

d   **Why is a ban on smoking important in a service station?**

....

1

Q8d

e   When petrol is spilled it smells strongly and soon disappears.

An oil spill does not smell and does not disappear.
Explain these differences.

....

....

....

2

Q8e

9 Finish the diagram below by adding the correct words from the list below.

condensing   cooling   evaporating   freezing   melting

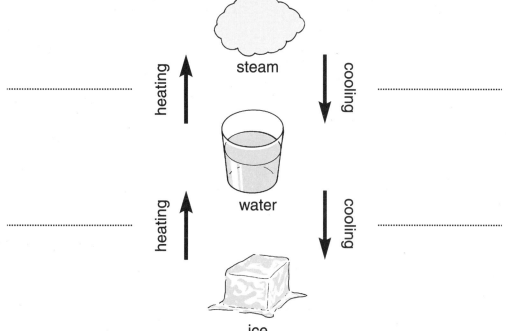

10 The diagram shows part of the water cycle.

a What is happening at points A and B on the diagram?

A ....

B ....

b Draw an arrow on the diagram to show one other way that water leaves the Earth and forms clouds.

Letts

Which is the best duvet?

11 A test was carried out to compare three duvets, **A**, **B**, and **C**, to find out which one would keep in the heat best.

A hot-water bottle was filled with boiling water and placed on a bed under one of the duvets. After four hours, the bottle was removed and the temperature of the water measured. This was repeated with the other duvets.

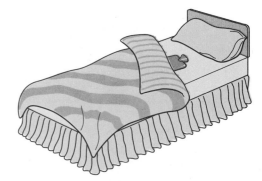

The results were:

Duvet	Temperature after four hours
A	55°C
B	58°C
C	65°C

a **What would you use to measure the temperature of the water after four hours?**

....

b **Why does the temperature of the water in the bottle drop?**

....

....

c
(i) **Which duvet is the best?**

Duvet ....

(ii) **Explain your answer.**

....

d **Suggest THREE things which should be done to make sure it is a fair test.**

(i) ....

(ii) ....

(iii) ....

Q11a **1**

Q11b **1**

Q11c(i) **1**

Q11c(ii) **1**

Q11d **3**

Materials

12   Here are some materials we use.

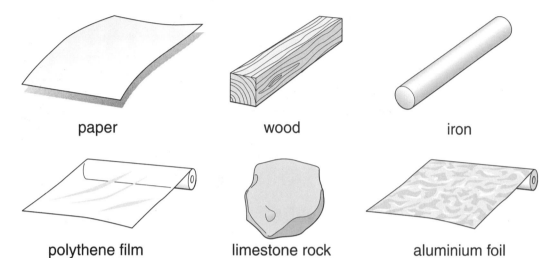

paper   wood   iron

polythene film   limestone rock   aluminium foil

a   **Finish the table showing some of the properties of these materials.**

Material	Easy to bend	Attracted to a magnet	Hard	See-through
wood	✗	✗	✗	✗
paper	✓	✗	✗	✗
iron				
polythene				
limestone				
aluminium				

4

Q12a

b   **Write down THREE of these materials which burn when heated in a flame.**

(i) ....

(ii) ....

(iii) ....

3

Q12b

c   **Write down ONE material which melts when heated in a flame.**

....

1

Q12c

29

Letts

Electricity

13   The diagram shows a battery and a bulb.

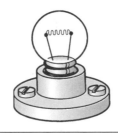

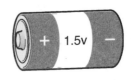

1

Q13a

a   **Draw TWO wires on the diagram to show how you could make the bulb light up.**

b   The next diagram shows a bulb and a motor.

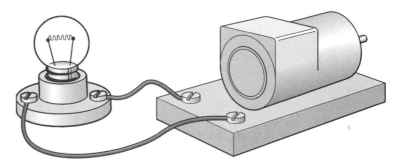

1

Q13b(i)

(i)   **What else is needed to make the bulb light up?**

....

1

Q13b(ii)

(ii)   **Draw it on the diagram.**

....

14   Here are three circuits with a battery, a motor, a switch and a bulb.

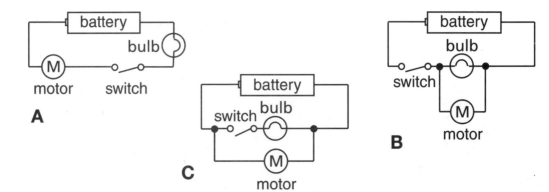

a

> Which circuit has a switch that controls the bulb only?

....

b

> In which circuits will the motor still work if the bulb is unscrewed?

....

15 The diagrams each show a bulb, a battery and two switches.

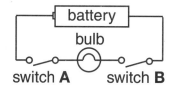

circuit 1   circuit 2

a

> Complete the table to show when each bulb is *on* or *off*.

Circuit 1			Circuit 2		
Switch A	Switch B	Bulb on or off	Switch A	Switch B	Bulb on or off
off	off		off	off	
on	off		on	off	
off	on		off	on	
on	on		on	on	

b

> Complete the sentences by filling in the missing words.

(i) To light the bulb in circuit 1, switch **A** .... switch **B** need to be pressed.

(ii) To light the bulb in circuit 2, switch **A** .... switch **B** needs to be pressed.

Electricity

16 Here are three circuits which each have two bulbs and two switches.

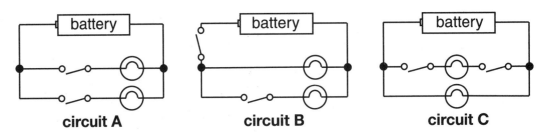

circuit A   circuit B   circuit C

1

Q16a

a | **In which circuit does each bulb have its own switch?**

✎ ....

1

Q16b

b | **Which circuit has a bulb that is *on* when both switches are *off*?**

✎ ....

2

Q16c

c | **Which TWO circuits have a bulb that only lights up when *both* switches are *on*?**

✎ ....

17 Sarah shines a torch at a mirror.

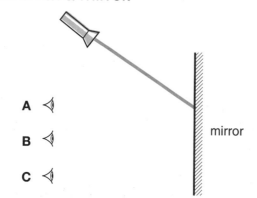

A ◁

B ◁

C ◁

mirror

a **What happens to the light when it hits the mirror? Underline the best word.**

affected   deflected   reflected   tilted

1
Q17a

b **Which eye in the drawing is in the best place to see the light after it hits the mirror?**

....

1
Q17b

18 **Underline the things in the list that *give out* light.**

book   candle   mirror   radio   Sun   television

1
Q18

19 Ravi uses a torch and some cardboard shapes to make shadow pictures on a wall.

Why is cardboard a good material for making shadow pictures?

Write down TWO reasons.

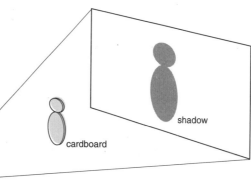

cardboard

shadow

(i) ....

1
Q19(i)

(ii) ....

1
Q19(ii)

20 After dark, Paula sits in her bedroom reading her book.

| Explain how Paula sees her book. |

....

....

....

3
Q20

21 Petra looks at a burning candle.

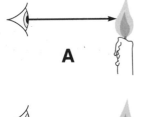

A

B

C

D

| Which diagram shows how she sees the candle? |

1
Q21

....

22 The Moon does not give out light.

| Explain how, on a clear night, you can see the Moon. |

2
Q22

....

....

Hearing

23 When a note is played on a piano a hammer hits a string. This makes the string move.

The pictures show the movement of the string. The arrows show which way the string is moving.

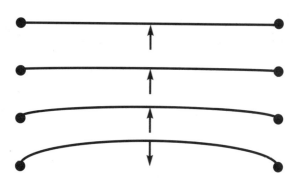

a | **Underline the word that *best* describes the movement of the string.**

acceleration   rotation   vibration

Q23a **1**

b The strings on a piano each play a different note.

| **Write down <u>TWO</u> ways in which piano strings can be different from each other.**

(i) ....

(ii) ....

Q23b **2**

Hearing

24 Tony makes a musical sound by blowing through a drinking straw.

2
Q24a

a **How does the sound change when he cuts the end off the straw to make it shorter?**

....

....

1
Q24b

b **What should Tony do to make the sound louder?**

....

....

1
Q24c

c Tony's mother is in the same room as Tony, listening to him playing his toy.

How does the sound travel from the straw to her ears?

....

....

1
Q24d

d Tony's sister is in the room next to Tony. She can hear the sound Tony makes, even though the door is closed.

Explain how Tony's sister can hear the sound.

....

....

Test C
Plants

1 Plants make their own food in a process called **photosynthesis**. The diagram illustrates photosynthesis.

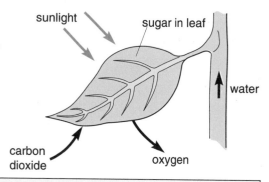

a **Name the energy source for photosynthesis.**

....

3
Q1a

b **Name the two substances that a plant uses to make food.**

....

....

2
Q1b

c **Write down the name of the food that the plant makes.**

....

1
Q1c

d **Write down THREE reasons why photosynthesis is important for all living things.**

(i) ....

(ii) ....

(iii) ....

3
Q1d

2 The diagram shows a plant cell.

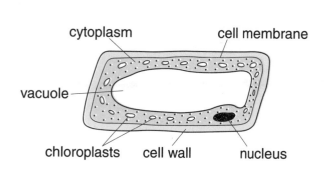

a **Explain why a plant cell has a cell wall.**

....

1
Q2a

Plants

b | What important process takes place in the chloroplasts?

 ....

c | Describe the job of the nucleus.

....

d | Draw and label a diagram of an animal cell.

The body

3 a | Choose words to complete the sentence about breathing.

air   carbon dioxide   nitrogen   oxygen

When we breathe in, ...

is taken into the lungs. The lungs

absorb .... and give

out waste ....

b | Write down **TWO** changes that happen to blood as it passes through the lungs.

(i) ....

(ii) ....

Rusting of iron and steel

4   A rusting experiment was carried out with three test tubes.

Each test tube contained a steel nail.

The tubes were left for a week.

The test tubes are shown in the diagram below.

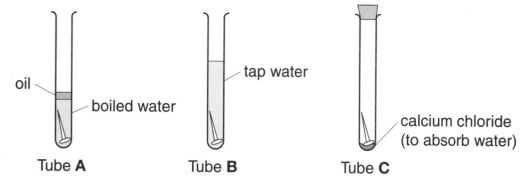

oil
boiled water
Tube **A**

tap water
Tube **B**

calcium chloride
(to absorb water)
Tube **C**

After a week, only the nail in tube **B** had rusted.

a | **Explain why rusting did not take place in tube A.** |

....

....

2
Q4a

b | **Explain why rusting did not take place in tube C.** |

....

....

2
Q4b

Iron and steel can be painted to prevent rusting.

c | **Apart from painting, write down TWO ways of preventing iron and steel from rusting.** |

(i) ....

(ii) ....

2
Q4c

Rusting of iron and steel

1

Q5(i)

1

Q5(ii)

5 **Write down TWO things needed for iron or steel to rust.**

 (i) ....

(ii) ....

6 Rock salt is put onto the roads during the winter to melt ice and snow.

What problem does this cause for car owners?

1

Q6

 ....

....

....

Respiration

7 Animals and plants both **respire**. Energy for movement comes from respiration in the muscles.

> **Choose words from the list to answer *a* and *b*.**

carbon dioxide   chlorophyll   glucose   nitrogen
oxygen   starch   water

a | **Name the two substances that muscles use when they respire.**

....

....

2
Q7a

b | **Name the two waste products of respiration.**

....

....

2
Q7b

c | **Describe how each of the waste products is removed from the body.**

....

....

2
Q7c

Types of reaction

8   Copper oxide is formed when copper carbonate is split up by heating. Carbon dioxide is also produced.

a   Underline the type of reaction taking place when copper carbonate is heated.

combustion   oxidation

reduction   thermal decomposition

1
Q8a

b   Write a word equation for the reaction taking place.

2
Q8b

 .... $\longrightarrow$ .... + ...

....

c   When hydrogen is passed over black copper oxide, a reaction takes place.

The word equation for the reaction is:

copper oxide + hydrogen → copper + hydrogen oxide

2
Q6c(i)

(i) | **What is meant by *oxidation* and *reduction*?** |

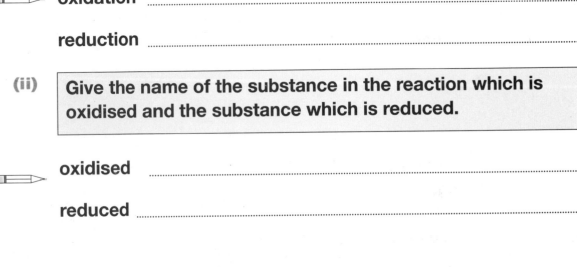
oxidation ....

reduction ....

(ii) | **Give the name of the substance in the reaction which is oxidised and the substance which is reduced.** |

2
Q6c(ii)

oxidised ....

reduced ....

Elements

9 Iron and sulphur are **elements**.

When iron is burned in oxygen, iron oxide is formed.
Iron oxide has a pH value of 7.

When sulphur is burned in oxygen, sulphur oxide is formed.
Sulphur oxide has a pH value of 4.

a
> **What does this information tell you about iron and sulphur?**

iron ....

sulphur ....

2
Q9a

b Iron and sulphur powders can be mixed together to give a **mixture** of iron and sulphur.

> **How could iron be separated from a mixture of iron and sulphur?**

....

....

2
Q9b

c When a mixture of iron and sulphur is heated a chemical reaction takes place.

> **Give the name of the compound formed.**

....

1
Q9c

d In the diagram below:

● stands for an iron atom; ● stands for a sulphur atom.

A

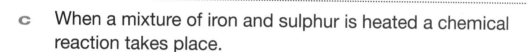
B

C

> **Choose the letter A, B or C which represents the following.**

1
Q9d(i)

(i) A mixture of iron and sulphur ....

(ii) A compound of iron and sulphur ....

1
Q9d(ii)

MARKS

Growth

10 Children in the same class at school can be very different in height, as the drawing shows.

| Write down **TWO** reasons which could explain why Darren is taller than Paul. |

Darren

Paul

2
Q10

 (i) ....

(ii) ....

Rocks

11 Granite is a rock produced when liquid rock from the inside of the Earth cools and crystallises.

| **Which of the following statements about granite are correct?** |

A Granite is a soft rock which easily crumbles.

B Energy is given out when granite crystallises.

C It is easy to melt granite.

D Crystals can be seen in a piece of granite.

2
Q11

....

12 The diagram shows two carbon rods connected to a battery. The carbon rods are in copper sulphate solution. The solution contains both positively and negatively charged particles.

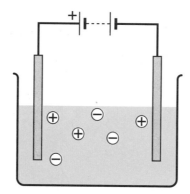

> **Explain what happens when a current passes through the solution.**

Q12

....

....

13 The diagram shows a circuit with a bulb and a motor.

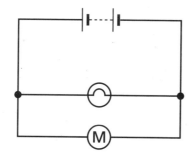

a
> **Mark an A in a position where you would place an ammeter to measure the current in the bulb only.**

Q13a

b
> **Mark a B in a position where you would place an ammeter to measure the total current in the motor and the bulb.**

Q13b

Forces

14 The arrows show the horizontal forces on a car travelling forwards on a level road.

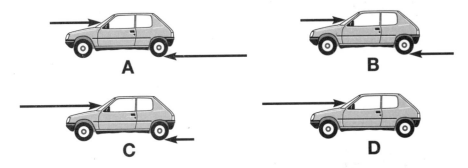

A   B

C   D

a **Which diagram or diagrams show a car that is:**

 (i) speeding up? ....

(ii) slowing down? ....

(iii) travelling at a steady speed? ....

b **The forwards arrow represents the driving force. What force does the backwards arrow represent?**

 ....

c When the car travels onto a patch of mud, the wheels spin round but the car does not move forwards.

Explain why the car does not move forwards.

 ....

15   The drawing shows the positions of the three planets that are closest to the Sun.

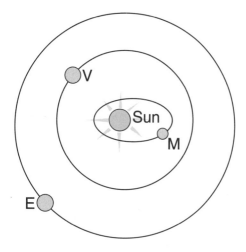

a   **Write down TWO differences between the orbit of planet M and the orbit of planet V.**

1
Q15a(i)

(i) ....

(ii) ....

1
Q15a(ii)

b   The times taken by the planets to orbit the Sun are shown in the table.

Orbit time	Planet
88 Earth days	
365 Earth days	
225 Earth days	

3
Q15b

Write the letter of the correct planet next to its orbit time.

Light

16 When light passes through glass it is **refracted**.

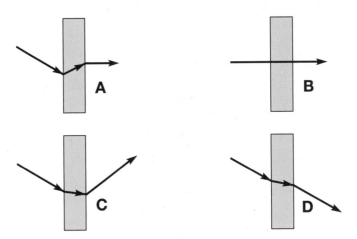

> **Which diagrams show how light travels through a window?**

2
Q16

....

17 Rainbows are sometimes seen when light passes through drops of water.

> **Tick the statement which explains how rainbows are formed.**

1
Q17

A The water drops add different colours to the light. ☐

B Light looks different colours when it is wet. ☐

C The water drops split the white light into different colours. ☐

D The water drops take colours out of the light. ☐

HOW TO MARK THE QUESTIONS

When marking your child's test remember that the answers given are sample answers. You must look at your child's answers and judge whether they deserve credit. Award the mark if the answer deserves credit.

At the end of Key Stage 2 your child's spelling may show a number of errors. Do not mark any answer wrong because the the words are misspelt. Read the word aloud and if it sounds correct award the mark. For example, 'desolv' would be acceptable for 'dissolve'.

When you go through the test with your child try to be positive. Look for good things that have been done in addition to showing where errors have been made.

Enter your child's marks onto the chart on page 66, and then refer to the section below.

USING THE MARKING CHART

Add up the number of marks awarded for Test A. Do the same for Test B. Look at the chart on page 66 and read off the corresponding level of marks below. If your child has scored Level 5 in Tests A and B, he or she can then have a go at Test C. The number of marks in Test C needed to gain a Level 6 is shown below.

Mark scored in Test A ☐   Mark scored in Test C ☐

Mark scored in Test B ☐

(Before Level 6 can be awarded on Test C, your child must have achieved Level 5 in Tests A and B)

Total ☐

Marks	Level	National comparison for age group
22 or below	1 and 2	Working towards target
23–37	3	Working towards target
38–65	4	Achieved target
66 or above	5	Exceeds target
Test C: 42 or above	6	Exceptional performance

Visit to the pond — *Pages 1–2*

1a **(i)** Water plants — *1 mark*

(ii) The heron could die but it is more likely that the heron would move elsewhere to find food. — *Either answer: 1 mark*

b Grass → rabbit → stoat — *3 marks*

c Eat food
Breathe
Lose waste materials
Award three marks if all correct and none incorrect.
Award two marks if two correct and one wrong.
Award one mark if one correct and two wrong. — *3 marks*

d Cool
Damp
Safe from predators
Supply of food
Not in direct light or dark
Any three: one mark each — *3 marks*

Total 11 marks

Note to parent

There may be other answers to **d**. You need to look at the answer and award marks if it seems reasonable.

In the wood — *Page 3*

2a **(i)** There is not much light. — *1 mark*

(ii) There is not much water. — *1 mark*

Note to parent

Give a mark for 'lack of nutrients' in **a** but not for 'lack of food'.

b They grow and flower in spring, when there is the most light under the trees. — *1 mark*

c Its long, pointed beak enables it to eat insects hidden in holes in the bark. — *1 mark*

d They rot or cause the leaves to decay. — *1 mark*

Total 5 marks

The body — *Pages 4–5*

3 a **A** kidney — *1 mark*
B brain — *1 mark*
C heart — *1 mark*
D lung — *1 mark*
E stomach — *1 mark*

b **C** — *1 mark*
E — *1 mark*
A — *1 mark*
D — *1 mark*
B — *1 mark*

Total 10 marks

4a 110 cm – Allow answer between 108 cm and 112 cm. *1 mark*
  b 40 cm – Allow answer between 38 cm and 42 cm. *1 mark*
  c 11 *1 mark*
  d **x** at 0 years and 50 cm *1 mark*
  e **x** at 3 years and 80 cm *1 mark*
  f Between birth and three years old *1 mark*

Total 6 marks

Note to parent

The steeper line between birth and three years shows that the girl was growing faster. This question tests your child's skill in handling data. This is an important scientific skill which is often neglected.

A new life   Page 6

5a Infancy, childhood, adolescence, young adulthood, middle age, retirement *1 mark*
  b Young adulthood *1 mark*
  c Infancy, childhood and adolescence *1 mark*

Total 3 marks

Making pure water   Pages 7–8

6a **(i)** Closely woven cloth or cloth with small holes in it *1 mark*
   (ii) Most of the mud (or solid particles) will stay on the cloth. *1 mark*
   (iii) Dissolved impurities *1 mark*

Note to parent

Few children will give this answer but it is important for them to realise that impurities can be present, dissolved in the water. Because they cannot be seen, they are often forgotten. Use the example of salt water, which looks like water but tastes salty because of the dissolved salt.

   (iv) Filtering or filtration *1 mark*
  b **(i)** The water boils or turns to steam. *1 mark*
   (ii) Steam condenses or turns to water. *1 mark*
   (iii) To keep the plastic bottle cool. *1 mark*

Note to parent

Condensation of steam produces a lot of heat. The wet cloth keeps the plastic bottle cool.

   (iv) Distillation *1 mark*
   (v) They have remained in the tin can. *1 mark*

Note to parent

This question is testing your child's understanding of the processes of filtration and distillation but in a slightly different context. Distillation involves two processes – boiling followed by condensation.

Total 9 marks

Making a car   **Pages 9–10**

7a is a conductor of electricity.   *1 mark*
  b is squashy.   *1 mark*
  c is easily shaped.   *1 mark*
           Total 3 marks

Note to parent

These questions are designed to get your child to pick a reason why certain materials are used for certain jobs. You will notice in **a**, for example, that all three possible answers are correct descriptions of copper, but it is important to pick the reason which fits. With electric wiring, obviously electrical conductivity is essential.

8 'Made' boxes should be ticked for glass, steel, plastic.
  'Natural' boxes should be ticked for water and wood.
  Award one mark for each correct answer. Do not penalise incorrect answers
  unless both 'Made' and 'Natural' boxes are ticked for one material.
  Then award nothing for that material.   *5 marks*
           Total 5 marks

Note to parent

If your child has made the common mistake of ticking both boxes for one material, remind him or her of the importance of following the instructions then checking.

9b liquid   *1 mark*
    because it can flow easily   *1 mark*
  c gas   *1 mark*
    because it can be squashed easily   *1 mark*
           Total 4 marks

Note to parent

This question requires your child to use information in the table and not just to recall the properties of solids, liquids and gases. With **b** there is no problem as only one property is suitable but in **c** a correct choice has to be made.

Containers   **Page 11**

10 a Glass, plastic (or the name of a plastic, e.g. polythene), metal (or the name of a metal, e.g. steel), cardboard (or waxed paper)
    Award one mark for each correct answer up to a maximum of three.   *3 marks*

b

See-through	Not see-through
bleach	milk
lemonade	gloss paint
lime	juice

           2 marks

Total 5 marks

Dissolving   *Pages 12–13*

11 a *Any two of the following:*
Heat the water.
Stir the mixture.
Grind up the crystals into a fine powder.
Use a larger volume of water.   *2 marks*
b The solution is blue in colour.   *1 mark*
c Copper sulphate crystals (accept solid)   *1 mark*
d The crystals would be smaller in size.   *1 mark*
e Add the mixture to water.   *1 mark*
Copper oxide does not dissolve but copper sulphate does.   *1 mark*
Filter to remove the copper oxide.   *1 mark*
Evaporate.   *1 mark*

or

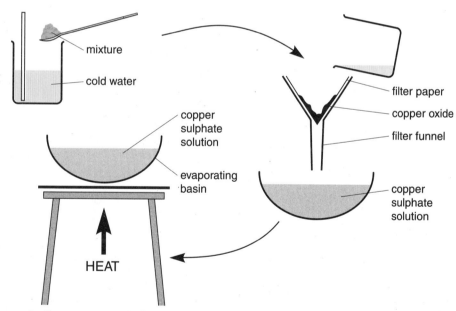

1 mark for each diagram; 1 mark for labelling.

Total 9 marks

Pages 14–15

12 a The circle should be between the two in the drawing, and higher in the window. *1 mark*

b

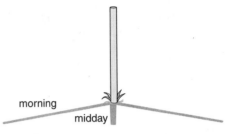

morning

midday

Award one mark for each shadow drawn correctly. *2 marks*

Total 3 marks

Note to parent

This question is testing whether your child knows that when the Sun is low in the sky the shadows are long and they become shorter as the Sun gets higher.

13 23 June *1 mark*

Total 1 mark

14 a The right-hand part of the Earth should be shaded. *1 mark*

b The Earth turns round *1 mark*

On its own axis. *1 mark*

Total 3 marks

15 Sun: a football *1 mark*

Earth: a tennis ball *1 mark*

Moon: a table-tennis ball *1 mark*

Total 3 marks

Note to parent

This question is testing whether your child is aware of the relative sizes of the bodies, as well as the spherical shape.

Pages 16–18

16 a The Earth's pull *or* gravity *or* the weight of the leaves *1 mark*

b Air resistance *1 mark*

c bigger than *1 mark*

equal to *1 mark*

Total 4 marks

Note to parent

A common error is to think that the force in the direction of travel is always bigger.

17 (i) Push it *1 mark*

(ii) Pull it *1 mark*

Total 2 marks

18 a It gets less *or* it slows down. *1 mark*

b The Earth (*or* gravity) pulls it. *1 mark*

Note to parent

Children often talk about gravity as if it were an object. To avoid confusion, they should be encouraged to use the phrase 'the Earth's pull'.

c E	pointing downwards	*1 mark*
A	pointing upwards	*1 mark*
d	The Earth's pull	*1 mark*
e	The ball speeds up as it falls.	*1 mark*

Note to parent

Do not give a mark for 'because it is falling down'. The direction of travel does not give any information about the forces.

Total 6 marks

19 a	It will go up.	*1 mark*
b	Awareness that there is an upward force.	*1 mark*
	Awareness that there is an downward force.	*1 mark*
	The upward force is bigger.	*1 mark*

Note to parent

Your child could answer this question at one of three levels. A simple answer such as 'because there is a force pushing it up' would gain one mark, whereas a fully correct answer 'the upward force is bigger than the downward force' gains three marks.

Total 4 marks

20 a	It becomes small *or* it is squashed.	*1 mark*

Note to parent

The question is testing whether the child knows that the shape of the spring changes, so do not give the mark for 'it moves down'.

b	Because of the force pushing it down *or* the weight of the child.	*1 mark*

Total 2 marks

Fun with magnets   *Page 19*

21 a	The arrow should point from right to left.	*1 mark*
b	The left-hand side of the magnet should be shaded.	*1 mark*
c	An arrow pointing up	*1 mark*
	This arrow represents the upward pull of the magnet.	
d	One arrow to the left ←	*1 mark*
	One arrow to the right →	*1 mark*

Note to parent

This question is testing the direction of the forces; the relative size of the arrows does not matter here.

e	To the left	*1 mark*
f	Paper clip drawn in the centre of the gap between the magnets.	*1 mark*

Total 7 marks

TOTAL FOR TEST A 105 marks

1a Housefly   *1 mark*
  b Spider   *1 mark*
  c Dragonfly   *1 mark*
                                    Total 3 marks

Note to parent

Being able to use keys is an important scientific skill at this level. Your child will not be expected to construct a key in a KS2 test but will be expected to use one as we have done in this question. It is worthwhile spending some time drawing up a simple key with your child so that he or she understands the principles.

Take four ordinary household objects, e.g. a cup, saucer, drinking glass and plastic measuring jug. Look at the similarities and differences, e.g. material used to make them, use, whether or not they have a handle, whether they can be used to measure, etc. Then draw up a key and check that the key enables you to identify each object individually. To understand the principles you do not have to use complicated objects. Then get your child to make up one alone. Check it at the end.

2a   **A** – Fruit   **B** – Leaf   **C** – Root   **D** – Stem   *4 marks*

Note to parent

At first sight you might think it strange to call the bean a fruit. Biologists have a slightly different use of the word 'fruit' from the general public. The biological definition of a fruit is a fertilised ovary. It may not be edible. In the case of the bean the fertilised ovary becomes fleshy and can be eaten. In biological terms tomatoes and cucumbers are fruits. Fruits contain seeds.

  b   **A** – The fruit   *1 mark*
  c   **C** – The roots   *1 mark*
  d   Genes   *1 mark*
                                    Total 7 marks

3 a   Stamen   *1 mark*
   b (i) To attract the bees, etc., which will pollinate the flower   *1 mark*
     (ii) The colour and smell attract bees   *1 mark*
           When the bee enters the tube it is difficult for it to leave the flower
           without pollinating.   *1 mark*
                                    Total 4 marks

Note to parent

Part **b** requires detail to score full marks.

4 a (i)   Incisor: cuts food   *1 mark*
    (ii) Canine: rips or tears food   *1 mark*
   (iii) Molar: grinds food into small pieces   *1 mark*
    b   Incisor   *1 mark*

Canine teeth are also sharp but they have points rather than edges.

  c To prevent tooth decay   *1 mark*
  d By brushing with toothpaste   *1 mark*
  e Straight after meals   *1 mark*

                                                      Total 7 marks

5   *Any three of the following*:
      She does not have enough food.
      Her diet is not varied.
      She eats little protein.
      She does not eat enough fruit.
      She does not eat enough fresh vegetables.
      Her diet is mainly flour-based.   *3 marks*

                                                      Total 3 marks

Blood round your body   Page 24

6a The circulatory system   *1 mark*

Only give your child the mark if he or she has written 'circulatory' or 'circulation', but do not penalise spelling. Pupils working at Level 4 are expected to use scientific terms for major body organs.

  b The heart is the large organ in the middle of the chest.   *1 mark*
  c It pumps blood around the body.   *1 mark*
  d It takes oxygen and food to different parts of the body.   *1 mark*
       It removes waste products from body organs.   *1 mark*
  e *Any two of the following*:
      has more oxygen
      has more food
      has less carbon dioxcide or other waste materials
      is at a higher pressure   *2 marks*

These differences apply to most, but not all, arteries and veins.

                                                      Total 7 marks

7a 3 minutes   *1 mark*
  b Her pulse rate starts to go up.   *1 mark*
  c She stopped playing football or started to rest.   *1 mark*
  d 72 beats per minute.   *1 mark*

                                                      Total 4 marks

As well as testing whether your child understands how pulse rate is linked to rest and exercise, this question tests his or her skills in reading data from a graph.

The service station — *Pages 25–26*

8a burns; energy; waste gases; oxygen; combustion — *One mark for each answer. 5 marks*

b Solid fuel – charcoal *or* coal
Liquid fuel – petrol diesel *or* paraffin
Gas fuel – camping gas
All three correct: 2 marks; two correct: 1 mark — *2 marks*

c Lines from clay to bricks, sand to glass, wood to charcoal, crude oil to petrol
One mark for each answer. 4 marks

d Petrol is very flammable or catches fire easily. — *1 mark*

e Petrol evaporates much faster than oil. — *1 mark*
The vapour causes the smell. — *1 mark*

Total 14 marks

Note to parent

This question is testing whether your child knows that the 'disappearance' of the liquid is due to evaporation and that liquids with strong smells evaporate readily.

The water cycle — *Page 27*

9 *Words (in clockwise direction from top left-hand corner):*
evaporating
condensing
freezing
melting
All correct: 3 marks; three correct: 2 marks; two correct: 1 mark — *3 marks*

Total 3 marks

Note to parent

The key to understanding the water cycle comes from understanding the changes of state involving ice, water and steam (or water vapour).

10 a A – evaporation — *1 mark*
B – precipitation — *1 mark*
b Arrow from trees to clouds — *1 mark*

Total 3 marks

Which is the best duvet? — *Page 28*

11 a Thermometer — *1 mark*
b Energy is lost as heat through the duvet (and through the bed). — *1 mark*
c Duvet **C** — *1 mark*
The temperature fell less with **C** than with **A** or **B** — *1 mark*

Note to parent

This question requires your child to use the results in the table. It does not require any knowledge. He or she should be looking for the one which loses the least amount of heat, shown by the smallest drop in temperature.

d *Any three of the following*:
  Use the same volume (or mass) of boiling water.
  Use the same hot-water bottle.
  Use the same bed.
  Make sure the room temperature is the same each time.

3 marks
Total 7 marks

Materials   Page 29

12 a

Material	Easy to bend	Attracted to a magnet	Hard	See-through
wood	✗	✗	✗	✗
paper	✓	✗	✗	✗
iron	✗	✓	✓	✗
polythene	✓	✗	✗	✓
limestone	✗	✗	✓	✗
aluminium	✓	✗	✗	✗

There are sixteen answers. Award:
  4 marks if 13–16 are correct
  3 marks if 10–12 are correct
  2 marks if 7–9 are correct
  1 mark if 4–6 are correct

4 marks

b (i) Polythene (ii) paper (iii) wood

1 mark each in any order. 3 marks

c   Polythene

1 mark
Total 8 marks

Electricity   Pages 30–32

13 a   One wire should be drawn from the + side of the battery to one side of the bulb. A second wire should lead from the - side of the battery to the other side of the bulb.

1 mark

b (i) A battery

1 mark

  (ii) The battery should be drawn inserted in one of the connecting wires, so that a complete circuit is made.

1 mark
Total 3 marks

14 a Circuit **C**

1 mark

  b Circuit **B**

1 mark

   Circuit **C**

1 mark
Total 3 marks

15 a   Circuit 1: off, off, off, on   *2 marks*
           Circuit 2: off, on, on, on   *2 marks*
    b (i) and   *1 mark*
     (ii) or   *1 mark*
                 Total 6 marks

16 a **A**   *1 mark*
    b **C**   *1 mark*
    c **B** and **C**   *One mark each: 2 marks*
                 Total 4 marks

Note to parent

Do not deduct marks for wrong answers. If one answer is correct and one is wrong in **c** award one mark.

Seeing   **Pages 33–34**

17 a Reflected   *1 mark*
    b **C**   *1 mark*
                 Total 2 marks

Note to parent

To get the correct answer in **b**, your child needs to recognise that the light is reflected at the same angle when it hits the mirror.

18   Candle, Sun and television   *1 mark*
                 Total 1 mark

Note to parent

If your child answered 'mirror' this shows confusion between things that reflect light and sources of light.

19 (i) Cardboard can be cut into shapes.   *1 mark*
   (ii) Light does not pass through it.   *1 mark*
                 Total 2 marks

20   Light from the lamp reaches the book.   *1 mark*
     The book reflects light.   *1 mark*
     Light from the book enters the eye.   *1 mark*
                 Total 3 marks

Note to parent

There are three important points to emphasise here:
    Light travels out from a light source.
    Surfaces reflect light.
    We see things when light from them enters our eyes.

21   **C**   *1 mark*
                 Total 1 mark

Note to parent

This question is testing the first and last points emphasised in the note after Question 20.

22   Light comes from the Sun.   *1 mark*
It is reflected by the Moon.   *1 mark*
Total 2 marks

Note to parent

Your child may not appreciate that light comes from the Sun even at night. A model using a table lamp, a football and a tennis ball could help to explain this.

Hearing   *Pages 35–36*

23 a Vibration   *1 mark*
b *Two from*: longer/shorter; heavier/lighter; tighter/slacker   *One mark each: 2 marks*
Total 3 marks

Note to parent

Only award a mark for *one* of the answers from each pair given, e.g. do not award a mark for 'longer' and a mark for 'shorter'.

24 a The pitch changes.   *1 mark*
It becomes higher.   *1 mark*

Note to parent

Award your child the first mark for recognising that there is a change in pitch, even if he or she gives the wrong change; therefore 'it gets lower' is awarded one mark and 'it gets higher' is awarded two marks.

b Blow harder.   *1 mark*
c The sound travels through the air.   *1 mark*
d The sound travels through the walls or door.   *1 mark*
Total 5 marks

TOTAL FOR TEST B 105 marks

Plants — Page 37

1a The Sun — *1 mark*
b Carbon dioxide and water — *One mark each: 2 marks*
c Sugar — *1 mark*
d *Any three of the following*:
    It provides food for plants.
    Plants provide food for animals.
    It removes carbon dioxide from the atmosphere.
    It supplies oxygen to the atmosphere. — *One mark each: 3 marks*
Total 7 marks

Note to parent

Children working at Level 6 should realise that photosynthesis is important in maintaining the balance of gases in the atmosphere and in providing the food source for all living things.

2a The cell wall keeps the cell in shape or makes it strong. — *1 mark*

Note to parent

Childen working at Level 6 should appreciate that plants depend on cell walls for their rigidity.

b Photosynthesis — *1 mark*
c The nucleus controls the cell. — *1 mark*
d The important parts are: the cell membrane, the cytoplasm and the nucleus.

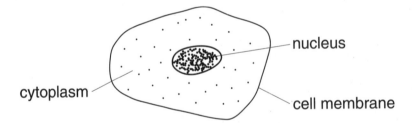

One mark for each correctly drawn and labelled: 3 marks
Total 6 marks

The body — Page 38

3a Air
    Oxygen
    Carbon dioxide — *3 marks*
b (i) It loses carbon dioxide. — *1 mark*
(ii) It gains oxygen. — *1 mark*

Note to parent

Do not give a mark for 'it gains air', but do give a mark for 'it loses water' if your child gives this answer instead of one of those given.

Total 5 marks

Rusting of iron and steel — *Pages 39–40*

4a Air (*or* oxygen) was removed from the water on boiling.   *1 mark*
Air (*or* oxygen) cannot get in through the oil.   *1 mark*

b Calcium chloride (or drying agent) removes water.   *1 mark*
Rusting does not take place in the absence of water.   *1 mark*

c Oiling, greasing, galvanizing (i.e. coating the steel with zinc), coating with plastic (e.g. washing-up racks), using a reactive metal such as magnesium in contact with the steel. (This is called sacrificial protecting as the magnesium corrodes in preference to the steel and is used to stop the legs of piers corroding.)   *Any two answers: 2 marks*
Total 6 marks

5 a (i) Oxygen *or* air   *1 mark*
  b(ii) Water *or* moisture   *1 mark*
Total 2 marks

6 Salt speeds up rusting and so can cause cars to rust faster.   *1 mark*
Total 1 marks

Respiration — *Page 41*

7 a Glucose and oxygen   *1 mark each: 2 marks*
  b Water and carbon dioxide   *1 mark each: 2 marks*
  c Carbon dioxide is removed by breathing.   *1 mark*
    Water is removed in urine or by breathing or sweating.   *1 mark*
Total 6 marks

Types of reaction — *Page 42*

8 a Thermal decomposition   *1 mark*
  b Copper carbonate $\longrightarrow$ copper oxide + carbon dioxide   *2 marks*
    Award one mark for the left-hand side and one mark for the right-hand side of the equation.

Note to parent

At Level 6 your child will be expected to write simple word equations. In this case it is a matter of using the information given.

  c (i) Oxidation is where a substance gains oxygen *or* loses hydrogen.   *1 mark*
    Reduction is the opposite of oxidation when a substance loses oxygen *or* gains hydrogen.   *1 mark*
  (ii) Oxidised – hydrogen   *1 mark*
    Reduced – copper oxide   *1 mark*
Total 7 marks

Note to parent

AT3 of the National Curriculum Science at Level 6 requires the understanding of many scientific terms. The meaning of the following should be clearly understood: decomposition, electrolysis, oxidation, reduction, fermentation, neutralisation, exothermic, endothermic, igneous, sedimentary, metamorphic, element and compound.

Elements **Page 43**

9a	Iron is a metal.	*1 mark*
	Sulphur is a non-metal.	*1 mark*

Note to parent

The most reliable test to see if an element is a metal or non-metal is to burn the element in oxygen and then test the oxide formed. If the oxide is acidic (pH less than 7), the element is a non-metal. If the oxide is neutral or alkaline (pH of 7 or greater), the element is a metal.

b	Use a magnet.	*1 mark*
	Iron sticks to the magnet and can be removed. Sulphur does not.	*1 mark*

Note to parent

Most pupils get the first mark but few go on to get the second. Probably in most cases they know the answer, and would give it if asked orally, but do not think to write it down. The question is worth two marks and they should be aware that 'use a magnet' is not a two-mark answer.

c	Iron sulphide	*1 mark*
d (i)	C	*1 mark*
(ii)	A	*1 mark*
		Total 7 marks

Growth **Page 44**

10	Darren's parents could be tall and he could have a better diet.	*2 marks*
		Total 2 marks

11	**B** and **D**	*2 marks*
	*Deduct one mark for each incorrect answer, e.g. **B** and **C** = 0, **A**, **B** and **D** = 1.*	

Note to parent

The wording of the question, and the fact that there are two marks allocated, suggests that more than one answer is required. For KS2, children should be familiar with rocks and be able to see similarities and differences. Often a local museum has samples of different types of rock. Children should be able to see the crystalline nature of igneous rocks, such as granite, and the layered structure of sedimentary rocks, such as sandstone. As an alternative to a museum, a church and churchyard will show different types of rock in use, e.g. marble, sandstone, limestone, granite, etc.

Total 2 marks

Electricity — Page 45

12 The positively charged particles move to the negative rod.   *1 mark*
The negatively charged particles move to the positive rod.   *1 mark*
Total 2 marks

13 a The **A** should be placed between one side of the bulb and a black dot.   *1 mark*

Note to parent

It does not matter which side of the bulb the ammeter is placed, since the current leaving the bulb is the same as the current that enters the bulb.

b The **B** should be placed between one side of the battery and a black dot.   *1 mark*
Total 2 marks

Forces — Page 46

14 a (i) **A**   *1 mark*
   (ii) **C** and **D**   *One mark each: 2 marks*
   (iii) **B**   *1 mark*
   b   The resistive force *or* air resistance   *1 mark*
   c   There is not enough friction between the wheels and the road.   *1 mark*
Total 6 marks

Note to parent

Children often get confused about forces that resist motion and they tend to use 'friction' to describe any resistive force. Friction is the force that opposes slipping or sliding.

The solar system — Page 47

15 a (i) **M**'s orbit is elliptical, **V**'s is circular.   *1 mark*
   (ii) **V**'s is longer *or* further from the Sun.   *1 mark*
   b   **M**   *1 mark*
          E   *1 mark*
          V   *1 mark*
Total 5 marks

Light — Page 48

16 **B** and **D**   *One mark each: 2 marks*
Total 2 marks

17 **C**   *1 mark*
Total 1 mark

TOTAL FOR TEST C 69 marks

Marking grid

Question	Marks available	Marks scored	Question	Marks available	Marks scored
1	11		12	3	
2	5		13	1	
3	10		14	3	
4	6		15	3	
5	3		16	4	
6	9		17	2	
7	3		18	6	
8	5		19	4	
9	4		20	2	
10	5		21	7	
11	9		Total	105	

Question	Marks available	Marks scored	Question	Marks available	Marks scored
1	3		13	3	
2	7		14	3	
3	4		15	6	
4	7		16	4	
5	3		17	2	
6	7		18	1	
7	4		19	2	
8	14		20	3	
9	3		21	1	
10	3		22	2	
11	7		23	3	
12	8		24	5	
			Total	105	
			Total A and B	210	

Question	Marks available	Marks scored	Question	Marks available	Marks scored
1	7		10	2	
2	6		11	2	
3	5		12	2	
4	6		13	2	
5	2		14	6	
6	1		15	5	
7	6		16	2	
8	7		17	1	
9	7		Total	69	